LER 2564

SUBTRACTING FRACTIONS WITH UNLIKE DENOMINATORS

by
Barbara Bando Irvin, Ph.D.

TABLE OF CONTENTS

INTRODUCTION

● ●

Subtracting Fractions With Unlike Denominators is part of a series of 32-page activity books developed to help students in grades 3-6 understand, compare, and perform operations on fractions. The activities in each book provide hands-on experiences using Fraction Tower® Cubes with 24 blackline master activity sheets. Students can build fraction towers, record their discoveries, and complete exercises on these activity pages. Refer to the scope and sequence chart on the inside front cover for the content of each book, and for the suggested grade levels.

The Teaching Notes on pages 4-6 offer explanations and suggestions to help students understand the activities. Selected Solutions on page 32 provide at least one solution for each problem. On the inside back cover, a Glossary is provided for quick reference of fraction terms. Students can make their own paper models of the Fraction Tower Cubes using copies of the Fraction Tower Chart on page 7. They can also use the Fraction Tower Chart as a workmat to build and compare fraction towers.

NCTM Standards

The fraction activities were developed using NCTM's *Curriculum and Evaluation Standards for School Mathematics* (1989) as a guide. Special attention was given to Standard 12 in grades K-4 and Standards 5, 6, and 7 in grades 5-8. They include the following goals for students:

- Develop concepts for fractions and mixed numbers.
- Develop and use order relationships for fractions.
- Develop number sense for fractions.
- Use models to find equivalent fractions.
- Use models to explore operations on fractions.

About the Fraction Tower Cubes

The set of Fraction Tower Cubes consists of 51 interlocking, proportional-sized cubes representing unit fractions $\frac{1}{12}, \frac{1}{10}, \frac{1}{8}, \frac{1}{6}, \frac{1}{5}, \frac{1}{4}, \frac{1}{3}, \frac{1}{2}$, and the number 1. They are color-coded in nine colors to match other Learning Resources fraction manipulatives: Deluxe Rainbow Fraction Circles, Deluxe Rainbow Fraction Squares, and Rainbow Fraction Tiles. This system enables students to make connections among different-shaped fractional parts as they work with different fraction models.

The set of 51 Fraction Tower Cubes includes:
- one red *whole*
- two pink *halves*
- three orange *thirds*
- four yellow *fourths*
- five green *fifths*
- six teal (blue-green) *sixths*
- eight blue *eighths*
- ten purple *tenths*
- twelve black *twelfths*

Unlike most other fraction manipulatives, the Fraction Tower Cubes are three-dimensional and can be snapped together to create a single piece. For example, five blue cubes can be snapped together to show the fraction $\frac{5}{8}$. Then the tower can be handled as one piece to compare it to another fraction, such as $\frac{3}{4}$, represented by snapping together three yellow cubes.

Free Exploration

Provide time for students to familiarize themselves with the Fraction Tower Cubes before doing any structured activities. Allow them to snap the cubes together and then unsnap the cubes to get a "feel" for them. Observe and listen to the students' comments. Ask some informal questions to assess their understanding of fractions.

Classroom Management

Students can work individually or in pairs to complete each activity. As students clean up after an activity, have them snap together the cubes to make same-color fraction towers, and place them back into the self-closing plastic containers. This is an easy way to check if any cubes are missing, and the set of Fraction Tower Cubes is ready to be used again.

HOW TO USE THE ACTIVITIES

It is very important that students have adequate time to understand the size of fractional numbers and the relationships between them. All too often, fraction activities are rushed or cut short in order to focus on the algorithms for performing the operations on fractions. The activities in this book focus on subtracting fractions and mixed numbers with unlike denominators. Use the activities to introduce, enhance, or even replace a classroom lesson. Discuss the students' ideas and solutions.

Workmat Page Format

The pages in this activity book resemble "workmats" so that students can physically manipulate fraction cubes in an adequate amount of space. The mats are designed to align the bottoms of the fraction towers for building and comparing fractions. The red cube is often displayed on the left side of the page to compare fraction towers to 1. These workmat pages help students connect actual fraction towers to pictorial images of them, and then to the written fraction. Horizontal and vertical formats help students draw and write their responses directly on the activity page without using another sheet of paper.

Many of the activities are arranged in a two-page layout. The pages may be duplicated for use in classrooms, or books may be purchased in sufficient numbers for each student to have his or her own. Students can use the Fraction Tower Chart on page 7 to make their own set of Fraction Tower Cubes. A transparency of the chart for the overhead projector can be used to build and compare fractions, improper fractions, and mixed numbers.

Materials Needed

The activities in Activity Book 5 require the following materials:
- two sets of Fraction Tower Cubes
- a box of crayons (colored pencils, markers)
- a pencil
- paper clip or clear spinner
- bag or sack
- 10 markers or counters (beans, coins, etc.)

Warm Up

The activities in Activity Books 1 and 2 focused on building and comparing fractions and mixed numbers. Activity Book 3 focused on adding and subtracting fractions and mixed numbers with like denominators. Activity Book 4 concentrated on adding fractions with unlike denominators. Before starting the activities in this activity book, do a quick review of the concepts in Books 1-4.

1. *What do you know?* Ask students to tell you what they know about fractions. Have them draw pictures and write a few sentences.

2. *Review equivalent fractions.* Build some one-color fraction towers that are as tall as $\frac{2}{3}$ ($\frac{2}{3}$: 2 orange cubes; $\frac{4}{6}$: 4 teal cubes; $\frac{8}{12}$: 8 black cubes).

3. *Review subtracting fractions and mixed numbers with like denominators.* $\frac{7}{8} - \frac{4}{8} = \frac{3}{8}$; $\frac{9}{10} - \frac{4}{10} = \frac{5}{10} = \frac{1}{2}$; $1 - \frac{7}{12} = \frac{12}{12} - \frac{7}{12} = \frac{5}{12}$; $1\frac{5}{6} - \frac{3}{6} = 1\frac{2}{6} = 1\frac{1}{3}$; $1\frac{1}{8} - \frac{7}{8} = \frac{9}{8} - \frac{7}{8} = \frac{2}{8} = \frac{1}{4}$. Build the first fraction (minuend) and then unsnap, or "take away" the cubes from the the second fraction (subtrahend). When subtracting from a whole or mixed number, the minuend must be expressed as an improper fraction. Always express the difference in simplest form.

4. *Review adding fractions with unlike denominators.* $\frac{2}{5} + \frac{5}{10} = \frac{4}{10} + \frac{5}{10} = \frac{9}{10}$; $\frac{5}{12} + \frac{1}{4} = \frac{5}{12} + \frac{3}{12} = \frac{8}{12} = \frac{2}{3}$; $\frac{4}{5} + \frac{1}{2} = \frac{8}{10} + \frac{5}{10} = \frac{13}{10} = 1\frac{3}{10}$; $\frac{5}{6} + \frac{2}{3} = \frac{5}{6} + \frac{4}{6} = \frac{9}{6} = 1\frac{3}{6} = 1\frac{1}{2}$; Build a fraction tower for each addend. Then build equivalent fraction towers in one color for the addends. Snap the two towers together, and express the sum in simplest form.

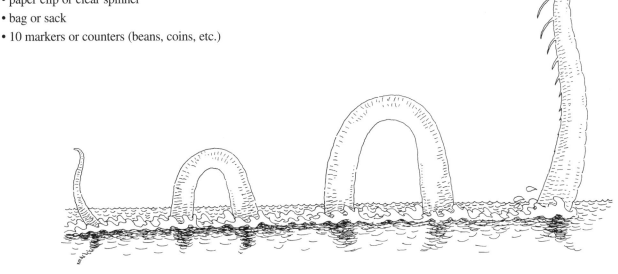

TEACHING NOTES

Subtracting fractions with unlike denominators is quite difficult for many students. With the carefully-sequenced activities in this book, students will experience increased success. Students were introduced to subtracting fractions with like denominators in Activity Book 3. The activities in this book build on that knowledge and help students find equivalent fraction towers for fractions with unlike denominators – and then find the difference.

The activities begin by subtracting unit and proper fractions. Activities increase in difficulty, and require students to use proper fractions and subtract with mixed numbers. The activities also include simplifying answers to lowest terms and/or mixed numbers. Subtraction is presented in two ways in this activity book: by "taking away," and by "comparison."

Note: The "build and draw" direction on the activity pages means to build a fraction with Fraction Tower Cubes, to trace (or draw) the cubes on the activity page, label the fraction towers, and then color the fraction tower the appropriate color with crayons, colored pencils, or markers. To color the black cubes, students may wish to simply shade them with a pencil so as not to color over the labeling.

The students need only one set of Fraction Tower Cubes for pages 8-17.

Subtracting Fractions (pages 8-9)

You may wish to do a quick review by finding one-color equivalent fraction towers for $\frac{1}{2}$, $\frac{1}{3}$, $\frac{1}{4}$, $\frac{1}{5}$, and $\frac{1}{6}$. Ask: What is $\frac{1}{3} = \frac{}{12}$? (4)

Each of the subtraction problems on these two pages includes a unit fraction as the amount to be taken away. The denominator of the unit fraction is either a factor or a multiple of the denominator of the other fraction. This makes it easier to express one fraction in terms of the other in this beginning activity. In the first problem on page 8, the $\frac{4}{5}$ must be changed to $\frac{8}{10}$ so $\frac{5}{12}$ can be taken away from it. In the second problem, $\frac{2}{3}$ must be changed to $\frac{8}{12}$, and $\frac{1}{4}$ changed to $\frac{3}{12}$ so that $\frac{3}{12}$ can be taken away from $\frac{8}{12}$.

Before students begin each problem, ask them to look carefully at the denominators. Then ask them what the common denominator should be in order to complete the subtraction process. Students must show and think of fraction towers having the same color. For problems 7 and 8 on page 9, ask students why these problems are a little more difficult than problems 1-6. (A common denominator must be found for both denominators.)

Subtracting Fractions and Simplifying Differences (pages 10-11)

In this activity, a common denominator must be found for one or both of the denominators in the problems. Also, the differences must be given in simplest form.

Students will need two sets of Fraction Tower Cubes for pages 12-31.

Comparing Fractions to Find Differences (pages 12-13)

Besides using the "take away" method for subtraction, students can "compare" fractions to find the difference. To compare fractions, build a one-color fraction tower for each fraction in the problem. If the towers are different colors, then find equivalent fraction towers so that both fraction towers can be compared using the same color.

The dashed lines on the fraction towers shown on page 12 act as a hint for students to find an equivalent fraction for that tower. In $\frac{7}{8} - \frac{1}{2}$, three dashed lines are shown on the fraction tower for $\frac{1}{2}$ to indicate four parts of $\frac{1}{2}$, which is equivalent to $\frac{4}{8}$. By comparing $\frac{7}{8}$ and $\frac{4}{8}$, $\frac{7}{8}$ is $\frac{3}{8}$ taller than $\frac{4}{8}$, or $\frac{1}{2}$. In the second problem $\frac{2}{3} - \frac{5}{12}$, the dashed lines shown on the tower for $\frac{2}{3}$ indicate the number of twelfths ($\frac{8}{12}$) that must be compared to $\frac{5}{12}$ in order to determine the difference between $\frac{2}{3}$ and $\frac{5}{12}$.

The two problems on page 13 also use comparison to find differences. With these problems, students must build the fraction towers and equivalent fraction towers.

Comparing Fractions to Find More Differences (pages 14-15)

More practice is provided to help students use the comparison method to find differences. Build fraction towers for both fractions in the problem. Then build equivalent fraction towers in the same color, and compare their heights.

Some students may find building equivalent fractions to be an easier way to do subtraction, rather than using the "take away" method. By comparing equivalent same-color fraction towers for each fraction in the problem, students can see the common denominator and the difference.

Estimating Differences (pages 16-17)

When estimating differences, it is important for students to think about the size of the fractions in a subtraction problem. Also, visualizing benchmarks such as 0, $\frac{1}{2}$, and 1 is necessary when considering the fractions in the problem, and the difference. Here are some examples to talk about before doing pages 16-17:

Problem: *Ask:*

$\frac{7}{8} - \frac{1}{4}$ Is $\frac{7}{8}$ nearest to 0, $\frac{1}{2}$ or 1? (1)

Is $\frac{1}{4}$ nearest to 0, $\frac{1}{2}$, or 1? (0 or $\frac{1}{2}$)

Do you think the difference is nearest to 0, $\frac{1}{2}$, or 1? ($\frac{1}{2}$, because one fraction is nearest to 1 and the other is less than $\frac{1}{2}$; Answer: $\frac{5}{8}$)

$\frac{11}{12} - \frac{3}{4}$ Is $\frac{11}{12}$ nearest to 0, $\frac{1}{2}$, or 1? (1)

Is $\frac{3}{4}$ nearest to 0, $\frac{1}{2}$, or 1? (1)

Do you think the difference is nearest to 0, $\frac{1}{2}$, or 1? (0, because both fractions are nearest to 1; Answer: $\frac{1}{6}$)

Do the problems on page 16 with the students, and ask them about $\frac{7}{12}$ and $\frac{1}{6}$ (*near $\frac{1}{2}$, near 0, difference about $\frac{1}{2}$*) in problem 1, and about $\frac{4}{5}$ and $\frac{3}{4}$ (*near 1, near 1, difference is near 0*) in problem 2. The exact difference ($\frac{5}{12}$) for problem 1 can be found using the Fraction Tower Cubes. The exact difference cannot be found for problem 2 using the cubes. For the second problem, students are forced to think about the estimate in terms of the two fractions of the subtraction problem. Each fraction is near 1, so the difference is near 0. Also encourage students to figure out that the common denominator is 20 and the difference is exactly $\frac{1}{20}$ ($\frac{4}{5} - \frac{3}{4} = \frac{16}{20} - \frac{15}{20} = \frac{1}{20}$, which is near 0.)

Some students may offer more refined estimates of $\frac{1}{4}$ or $\frac{3}{4}$ for the differences on page 17. Have them use 1 yellow ($\frac{1}{4}$), 1 pink ($\frac{1}{2}$), and 3 yellow ($\frac{3}{4}$) fraction towers to estimate the differences.

Subtracting From Mixed Numbers (pages 18-19)

Subtracting a fraction (or a mixed number) from a mixed number is not very different from subtracting a fraction from another fraction. In this activity, fractions are subtracted from fractions, and whole numbers are subtracted from whole numbers. The fraction parts of the problem must be expressed in same-color equivalent fractions before subtracting.

For $1\frac{7}{12} - \frac{1}{4}$, express $\frac{1}{4}$ as $\frac{3}{12}$ to have $1\frac{7}{12} - \frac{3}{12}$. Subtract to get the difference, $1\frac{4}{12} = 1\frac{1}{3}$.

Also consider subtracting a mixed number from a mixed number, such as $1\frac{2}{3} - 1\frac{1}{6}$. ($1\frac{2}{3} - 1\frac{1}{6} = 1\frac{4}{6} - 1\frac{1}{6} = \frac{3}{6} = \frac{1}{2}$.)

Doing mixed-number subtraction problems vertically helps students align the whole numbers and fractions. It also helps them remember to include the whole number in the difference.

$$\begin{array}{ll} 1\frac{7}{12} & \text{1 red, 7 black} \\ -\ \frac{1}{4} & -\ \text{1 pink} \end{array} \rightarrow \begin{array}{ll} 1\frac{7}{12} & \text{1 red, 7 black} \\ -\ \frac{3}{12} & -\ \text{3 black} \\ \hline 1\frac{4}{12} & \text{1 red, 4 black} \\ =1\frac{1}{3} & =\text{1 red, 1 orange} \end{array}$$

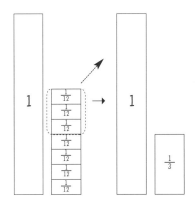

$$\begin{array}{ll} 1\frac{2}{3} & \text{1 red, 2 orange} \\ -\ 1\frac{1}{6} & -\ \text{1 red, 1 teal} \\ \hline ? & \end{array} \rightarrow \begin{array}{ll} 1\frac{4}{6} & \text{1 red, 4 teal} \\ -\ 1\frac{1}{6} & -\ \text{1 red, 1 teal} \\ \hline \frac{3}{6} & \text{3 teal} \\ =\frac{1}{2} & =\text{1 pink} \end{array}$$

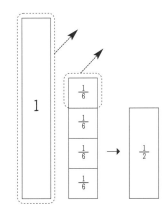

TEACHING NOTES

Regrouping and Subtracting Fractions With Like Denominators (pages 20-21)

This page provides a review of subtracting fractions from mixed numbers with like denominators. Students also focus on the regrouping process of the minuend using the "take away" method. For a problem like $1\frac{3}{8} - \frac{6}{8}$, build the mixed number fraction tower for $1\frac{3}{8}$ (1 red, 3 blue). Since there are only $\frac{3}{8}$ in the fraction part of $1\frac{3}{8}$, and $\frac{6}{8}$ must be taken away, more eighths are needed. Regroup, or trade, the 1 in $1\frac{3}{8}$ for $\frac{8}{8}$ to show $1\frac{3}{8} = \frac{11}{8}$. Now, $\frac{11}{8} - \frac{6}{8} = \frac{5}{8}$.

Some students may prefer to build their mixed number vertically as a two-color tower, and then compare to find the difference. Make a tall two-color fraction tower for $1\frac{3}{8}$ (1 red, 3 blue) and a fraction tower for $\frac{6}{8}$ (6 blue). To find the difference, change the two-color tower to a one-color tower (11 blue) to compare blue to blue, or eighths to eighths.

Regrouping and Subtracting Fractions With Unlike Denominators (pages 22-23)

Students must keep track of a lot of information when subtracting mixed numbers and fractions with unlike denominators and regrouping. First they must change all the fraction parts to equivalent fractions. Then they must observe whether the fraction parts can be subtracted from each other.

Find equivalent fractions:

$$
\begin{array}{llll}
1\frac{1}{2} & \text{1 red, 1 pink} \rightarrow & 1\frac{5}{10} & \text{1 red, 5 purple} \\
-\frac{4}{5} & \text{– 4 green} & -\frac{8}{10} & \text{– 8 purple} \\
\hline
& & \quad ? & \quad ?
\end{array}
$$

Regroup and subtract:

$$
\begin{array}{lll}
1\frac{5}{10} \rightarrow & \frac{15}{10} & \text{15 purple} \\
-\frac{8}{10} & -\frac{8}{10} & \text{– 8 purple} \\
\hline
& \frac{7}{10} & \text{7 purple}
\end{array}
$$

Subtracting With Mixed Numbers (pages 24-27)

More subtraction practice is provided on these four pages. All the problems require regrouping. After they have drawn pictures and written a few sentences about the problem, ask them to share their entries with their classmates.

Fraction Subtraction Action (page 28)
Addition and Subtraction Action (page 29)

Both pages use the "Bingo" game format to review the operations of addition and subtraction with fractional numbers. This is a self-correcting type of game. If students cannot find their differences in the grids, they must redo the problems.

On page 28, students review subtracting fractions and mixed numbers with unlike denominators, with or without regrouping. Page 29 provides a review of adding and subtracting fractions and mixed numbers with unlike denominators. Insist that students use Fraction Tower Cubes to find each sum or difference.

Spin-A-Difference Game (page 30)

Each player must start with a red and pink cube in order to subtract a fraction spun from $1\frac{1}{2}$. Since all of the subtraction problems generated with the spinner require regrouping, observe the players as they find the common denominator, and then regroup the mixed number to an improper fraction to find the difference. Solutions are provided on page 32.

For $1\frac{1}{2} - \frac{2}{3}$, students can proceed this way:

1. Build $1\frac{1}{2}$.   1 red, 1 pink

2. Then build $1\frac{3}{6}$.   1 red, 3 teal

3. Subtract $\frac{2}{3}$. Think: $\frac{2}{3} = \frac{4}{6}$.
   * Cannot unsnap 4 teal from 1 red, 3 teal. *

4. Build $\frac{9}{6}$ for $1\frac{3}{6}$.   9 teal

5. Subtract. Unsnap 4 teal.   5 teal (Answer: $\frac{5}{6}$)

Take Away Towers Game (page 31)

The comparison method is used to find the differences in this game. Players should quickly discover that they must try to build 2 fraction towers out of their 6 cubes. The two towers must be similar in height, in order to show a lesser difference than their opponent. In this game, it is possible to have a difference of 0. For example, if a player pulls 1 pink, 3 yellow, and 2 blue cubes during an "Average Game," the pink-blue tower ($\frac{1}{2} + \frac{2}{8} = \frac{3}{4}$) will match the height of the yellow tower ($\frac{3}{4}$) to show a difference of 0 ($\frac{3}{4} - \frac{3}{4} = 0$).

You may wish to have students write subtraction number sentences for their towers. This will show the sum of each tower and the difference between the two towers.

FRACTION TOWER CHART

red	pink	yellow	blue	orange	teal	black	green	purple
1	$\frac{1}{2}$	$\frac{1}{4}$	$\frac{1}{8}$	$\frac{1}{3}$	$\frac{1}{6}$	$\frac{1}{12}$	$\frac{1}{5}$	$\frac{1}{10}$
			$\frac{1}{8}$			$\frac{1}{12}$		$\frac{1}{10}$
		$\frac{1}{4}$	$\frac{1}{8}$		$\frac{1}{6}$	$\frac{1}{12}$	$\frac{1}{5}$	$\frac{1}{10}$
			$\frac{1}{8}$	$\frac{1}{3}$		$\frac{1}{12}$		$\frac{1}{10}$
	$\frac{1}{2}$	$\frac{1}{4}$	$\frac{1}{8}$		$\frac{1}{6}$	$\frac{1}{12}$	$\frac{1}{5}$	$\frac{1}{10}$
			$\frac{1}{8}$			$\frac{1}{12}$		$\frac{1}{10}$
		$\frac{1}{4}$	$\frac{1}{8}$	$\frac{1}{3}$	$\frac{1}{6}$	$\frac{1}{12}$	$\frac{1}{5}$	$\frac{1}{10}$
			$\frac{1}{8}$			$\frac{1}{12}$		$\frac{1}{10}$
1	$\frac{1}{2}$	$\frac{1}{4}$	$\frac{1}{8}$	$\frac{1}{3}$	$\frac{1}{6}$	$\frac{1}{12}$	$\frac{1}{5}$	$\frac{1}{10}$
			$\frac{1}{8}$			$\frac{1}{12}$		$\frac{1}{10}$
		$\frac{1}{4}$	$\frac{1}{8}$		$\frac{1}{6}$	$\frac{1}{12}$	$\frac{1}{5}$	$\frac{1}{10}$
			$\frac{1}{8}$	$\frac{1}{3}$		$\frac{1}{12}$		$\frac{1}{10}$
	$\frac{1}{2}$	$\frac{1}{4}$	$\frac{1}{8}$		$\frac{1}{6}$	$\frac{1}{12}$	$\frac{1}{5}$	$\frac{1}{10}$
			$\frac{1}{8}$			$\frac{1}{12}$		$\frac{1}{10}$
		$\frac{1}{4}$	$\frac{1}{8}$	$\frac{1}{3}$	$\frac{1}{6}$	$\frac{1}{12}$	$\frac{1}{5}$	$\frac{1}{10}$
			$\frac{1}{8}$			$\frac{1}{12}$		$\frac{1}{10}$

| red | pink | yellow | blue | orange | teal | black | green | purple |

SUBTRACTING FRACTIONS

Build a fraction tower for the first fraction. Then "take away" the fraction amount of the second fraction. You may have to build equivalent towers for either the first or second fraction, or both of them.

1. $\dfrac{4}{5} - \dfrac{1}{10} = \dfrac{\square}{10} - \dfrac{1}{10} = \dfrac{\square}{10}$

Think: $\dfrac{4}{5} = \dfrac{8}{10}$

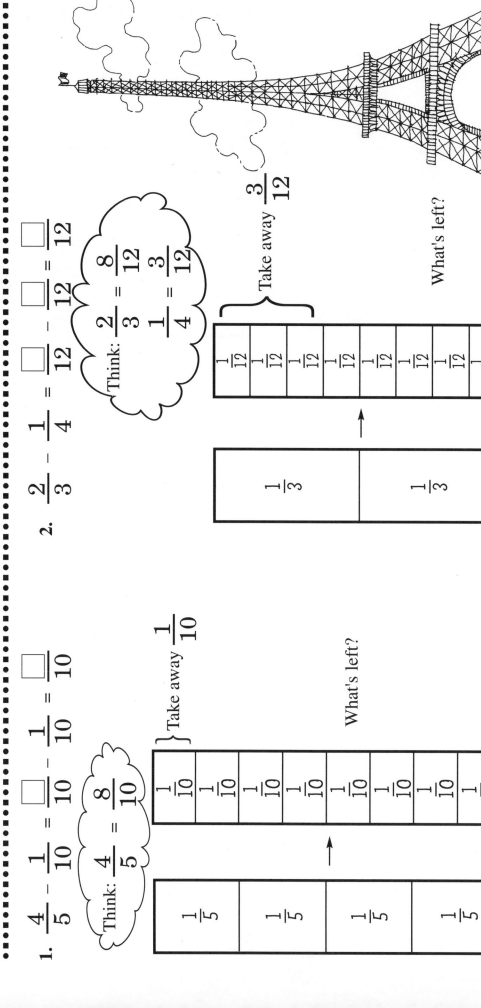

$\frac{1}{5}$
$\frac{1}{5}$
$\frac{1}{5}$
$\frac{1}{5}$

$\longrightarrow$

Take away $\dfrac{1}{10}$

$\frac{1}{10}$	$\frac{1}{10}$	$\frac{1}{10}$	$\frac{1}{10}$	$\frac{1}{10}$	$\frac{1}{10}$	$\frac{1}{10}$	$\frac{1}{10}$

What's left?

$\begin{array}{r} 4 \text{ green} \\ -\ 1 \text{ purple} \\ \hline ? \end{array} \longrightarrow \begin{array}{r} 8 \text{ purple} \\ -\ 1 \text{ purple} \\ \hline 7 \text{ purple} \end{array}$

2. $\dfrac{2}{3} - \dfrac{1}{4} = \dfrac{\square}{12} - \dfrac{\square}{12} = \dfrac{\square}{12}$

Think: $\dfrac{2}{3} = \dfrac{8}{12}$
$\dfrac{1}{4} = \dfrac{3}{12}$

$\frac{1}{3}$
$\frac{1}{3}$

$\longrightarrow$

Take away $\dfrac{3}{12}$

$\frac{1}{12}$	$\frac{1}{12}$	$\frac{1}{12}$	$\frac{1}{12}$	$\frac{1}{12}$	$\frac{1}{12}$	$\frac{1}{12}$	$\frac{1}{12}$

What's left?

$\begin{array}{r} 2 \text{ orange} \\ -\ 1 \text{ yellow} \\ \hline ? \end{array} \longrightarrow \begin{array}{r} 8 \text{ black} \\ -\ 3 \text{ black} \\ \hline 5 \text{ black} \end{array}$

SUBTRACTING MORE FRACTIONS

Name _____

Build the first fraction. Then subtract the second fraction.
Use equivalent fractions to find like denominators for both fractions.

	Problem	Equivalent Fractions	Difference
1.	$\dfrac{9}{12} - \dfrac{1}{6}$	$= \dfrac{\square}{12} - \dfrac{\square}{12}$	$= \dfrac{\square}{12}$
2.	$\dfrac{7}{8} - \dfrac{1}{2}$	$= \dfrac{\square}{8} - \dfrac{\square}{8}$	$= \dfrac{\square}{\square}$
3.	$\dfrac{2}{3} - \dfrac{1}{12}$	$= \dfrac{\square}{\square} - \dfrac{\square}{12}$	$= \dfrac{\square}{\square}$
4.	$\dfrac{1}{2} - \dfrac{1}{8}$	$= \dfrac{\square}{\square} - \dfrac{\square}{\square}$	$= \dfrac{\square}{\square}$
5.	$\dfrac{11}{12} - \dfrac{1}{2}$	$= \dfrac{\square}{\square} - \dfrac{\square}{\square}$	$= \dfrac{\square}{\square}$
6.	$\dfrac{1}{2} - \dfrac{1}{12}$	$= \dfrac{\square}{\square} - \dfrac{\square}{\square}$	$= \dfrac{\square}{\square}$

Try these.

	Problem	Equivalent Fractions	Difference
7.	$\dfrac{2}{3} - \dfrac{1}{2}$	$= \dfrac{\square}{\square} - \dfrac{\square}{\square}$	$= \dfrac{\square}{\square}$
8.	$\dfrac{5}{6} - \dfrac{1}{4}$	$= \dfrac{\square}{\square} - \dfrac{\square}{\square}$	$= \dfrac{\square}{\square}$

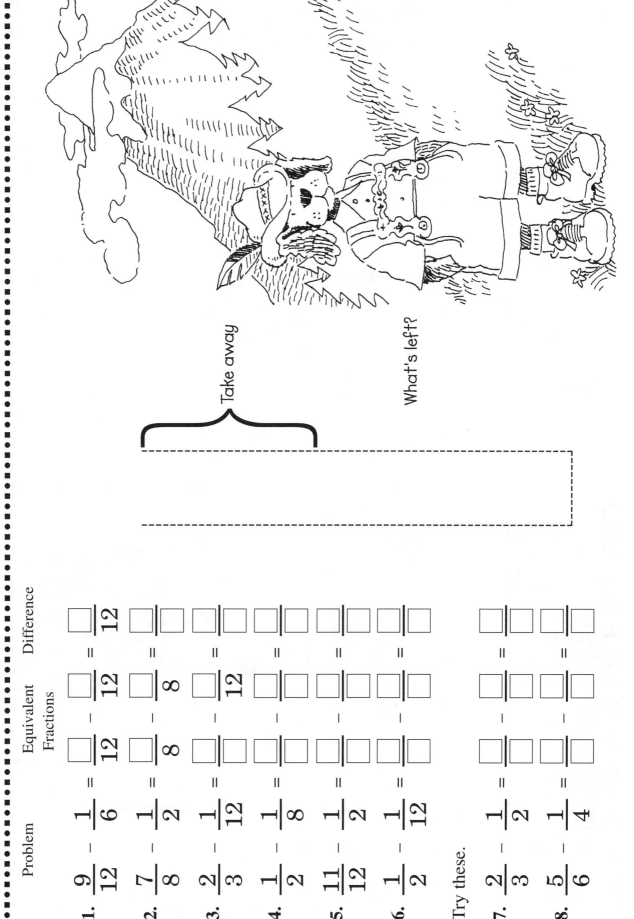

Take away

What's left?

SUBTRACTING FRACTIONS AND SIMPLIFYING DIFFERENCES

Name _____

Build a fraction tower for the first fraction. Then "take away" the fraction amount of the second fraction. You may have to build equivalent towers for either the first or second fraction, or both of them.

1. $\dfrac{11}{12} - \dfrac{2}{3} = \dfrac{11}{12} - \dfrac{\square}{12} = \dfrac{\square}{12} = \dfrac{\square}{4}$

Think: $\dfrac{2}{3} = \dfrac{8}{12}$

Simplify: $\dfrac{\square}{12} = \dfrac{\square}{4}$

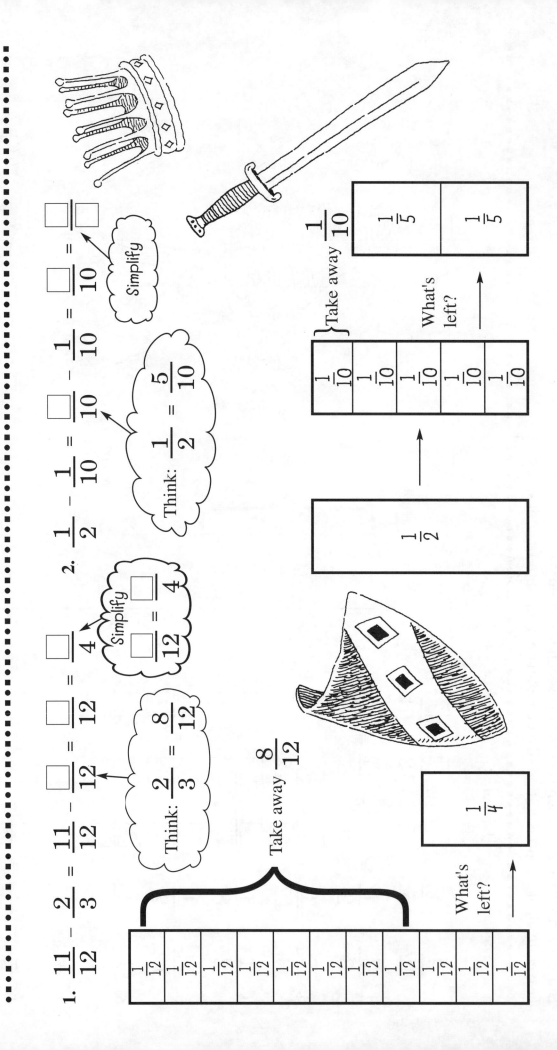

Take away $\dfrac{8}{12}$

| $\frac{1}{12}$ | $\frac{1}{12}$ | $\frac{1}{12}$ | $\frac{1}{12}$ | $\frac{1}{12}$ | $\frac{1}{12}$ | $\frac{1}{12}$ | $\frac{1}{12}$ | $\frac{1}{12}$ | $\frac{1}{12}$ | $\frac{1}{12}$ |

What's left? →

| $\frac{1}{4}$ |

2. $\dfrac{1}{2} - \dfrac{1}{10} = \dfrac{\square}{10} - \dfrac{1}{10} = \dfrac{\square}{10} = \dfrac{\square}{\square}$

Think: $\dfrac{1}{2} = \dfrac{5}{10}$

Simplify

Take away $\dfrac{1}{10}$

| $\frac{1}{10}$ | $\frac{1}{10}$ | $\frac{1}{10}$ | $\frac{1}{10}$ | $\frac{1}{10}$ |

| $\frac{1}{2}$ |

What's left? →

| $\frac{1}{5}$ | $\frac{1}{5}$ |

SUBTRACTING MORE FRACTIONS AND SIMPLIFYING MORE DIFFERENCES

Name _____

Build the first fraction. Then subtract the second fraction. Use equivalent fractions to find like denominators for both fractions. Simplify the difference when possible.

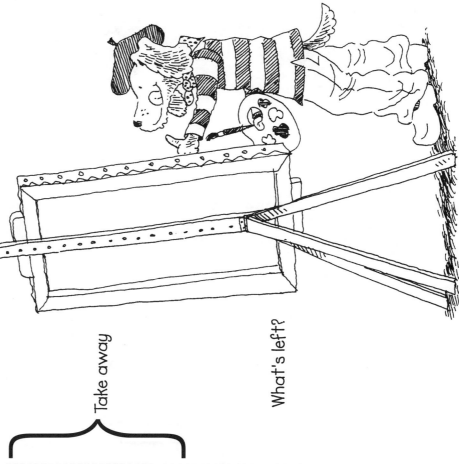

Take away

What's left?

Problem	Equivalent Fractions		Difference	Simplest Difference
1. $\dfrac{7}{10} - \dfrac{1}{5}$	$= \dfrac{\square}{10} - \dfrac{\square}{10}$		$= \dfrac{\square}{10}$	$= \dfrac{\square}{2}$
2. $\dfrac{1}{2} - \dfrac{1}{3}$	$= \dfrac{\square}{6} - \dfrac{\square}{6}$		$= \dfrac{\square}{6}$	
3. $\dfrac{9}{10} - \dfrac{1}{2}$	$= \dfrac{\square}{10} - \dfrac{\square}{10}$		$= \dfrac{\square}{10}$	
4. $\dfrac{7}{12} - \dfrac{1}{4}$	$= \dfrac{\square}{\square} - \dfrac{\square}{\square}$		$= \dfrac{\square}{\square}$	$= \dfrac{\square}{\square}$
5. $\dfrac{3}{4} - \dfrac{1}{6}$	$= \dfrac{\square}{\square} - \dfrac{\square}{\square}$		$= \dfrac{\square}{\square}$	
6. $\dfrac{5}{6} - \dfrac{3}{4}$	$= \dfrac{\square}{\square} - \dfrac{\square}{\square}$		$= \dfrac{\square}{\square}$	

COMPARING FRACTIONS TO FIND DIFFERENCES

Name _____

Another way to find the difference is to "compare" both fractions instead of "taking away." Build and draw fraction towers for both fractions. Then compare their heights to see how much taller one fraction tower is than the other.

●●●●●●●●●●●●●●●●●●●●●●●●●●●●

1. $\dfrac{7}{8} - \dfrac{1}{2} = \dfrac{7}{8} - \dfrac{4}{8} = \dfrac{\boxed{}}{8}$

Build $\dfrac{7}{8}$.

$\frac{1}{8}$	$\frac{1}{8}$	$\frac{1}{8}$	$\frac{1}{8}$	$\frac{1}{8}$	$\frac{1}{8}$	$\frac{1}{8}$

Difference is $\dfrac{3}{8}$

Build $\dfrac{1}{2}$.
Rebuild as $\dfrac{4}{8}$.

	$\frac{1}{2}$	

$\dfrac{7}{8}$ is taller than $\dfrac{1}{2}$

The difference
in their heights is $\dfrac{\boxed{3}}{\boxed{8}}$

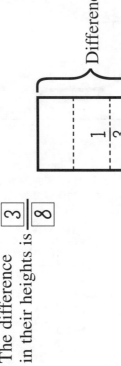

2. $\dfrac{2}{3} - \dfrac{5}{12} = \dfrac{\boxed{}}{12} - \dfrac{5}{12} = \dfrac{\boxed{}}{12} = \dfrac{\boxed{}}{4}$

Build $\dfrac{2}{3}$.
Rebuild as $\dfrac{8}{12}$.

$\frac{1}{3}$	$\frac{1}{3}$

Difference is $\dfrac{3}{12}$

Build $\dfrac{5}{12}$.

$\frac{1}{12}$	$\frac{1}{12}$	$\frac{1}{12}$	$\frac{1}{12}$	$\frac{1}{12}$

$\dfrac{2}{3}$ is taller than $\dfrac{5}{12}$

The difference
in their heights is $\dfrac{\boxed{}}{\boxed{}}$

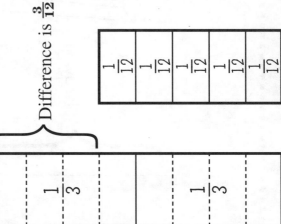

COMPARING FRACTIONS
TO FIND MORE DIFFERENCES

Build and draw fraction towers for both fractions. Then compare
their heights to see how much taller one fraction tower is than the other.

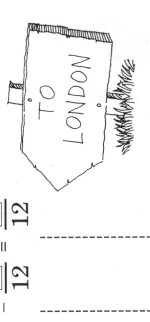

1. $\dfrac{3}{4} - \dfrac{1}{8} = \dfrac{\boxed{}}{8} - \dfrac{\boxed{}}{8} = \dfrac{\boxed{}}{8}$

Build $\dfrac{3}{4}$.
Rebuild as $\dfrac{6}{8}$.

Build $\dfrac{1}{8}$.

_____ is taller than _____.

The difference
in their heights is _____.

2. $\dfrac{2}{3} - \dfrac{1}{4} = \dfrac{\boxed{}}{12} - \dfrac{\boxed{}}{12} = \dfrac{\boxed{}}{12}$

Build $\dfrac{2}{3}$.
Rebuild as $\dfrac{8}{12}$.

Build $\dfrac{1}{4}$.
Rebuild as $\dfrac{3}{12}$.

_____ is taller than _____.

The difference
in their heights is _____.

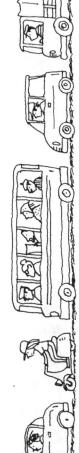

COMPARING FRACTIONS TO FIND EVEN MORE DIFFERENCES

Name _____

Build and draw fraction towers for both fractions. Then compare their heights to see how much taller one fraction tower is than the other. Simplify your answers.

• •

1. $\dfrac{11}{12}$ - $\dfrac{2}{3}$ = $\dfrac{\square}{\square}$ - $\dfrac{\square}{\square}$ = $\dfrac{\square}{\square}$

| $\frac{1}{12}$ | $\frac{1}{12}$ | $\frac{1}{12}$ | $\frac{1}{12}$ | $\frac{1}{12}$ | $\frac{1}{12}$ | $\frac{1}{12}$ | $\frac{1}{12}$ | $\frac{1}{12}$ | $\frac{1}{12}$ | $\frac{1}{12}$ |

Difference is $\frac{3}{12}$

| $\frac{1}{3}$ | $\frac{1}{3}$ |

Build $\frac{11}{12}$.

Build $\frac{2}{3}$.
Rebuild as $\frac{8}{12}$.

_____ is taller than _____.

The difference in their heights is _____.

2. $\dfrac{4}{5}$ - $\dfrac{3}{10}$ = $\dfrac{\square}{\square}$ - $\dfrac{\square}{\square}$ = $\dfrac{\square}{\square}$

| $\frac{1}{5}$ | $\frac{1}{5}$ | $\frac{1}{5}$ | $\frac{1}{5}$ |

| $\frac{1}{10}$ | $\frac{1}{10}$ | $\frac{1}{10}$ |

Build $\frac{4}{5}$.
Rebuild as _____.

Build $\frac{3}{10}$.

_____ is taller than _____.

The difference in their heights is _____.

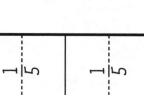

KEEP ON COMPARING FRACTIONS TO FIND DIFFERENCES

Name _____

Use the grids to build fraction towers for both fractions. Rebuild one or both fraction towers before comparing them to find the difference. Then compare their heights to see how much taller one fraction tower is than the other. Simplify your answers.

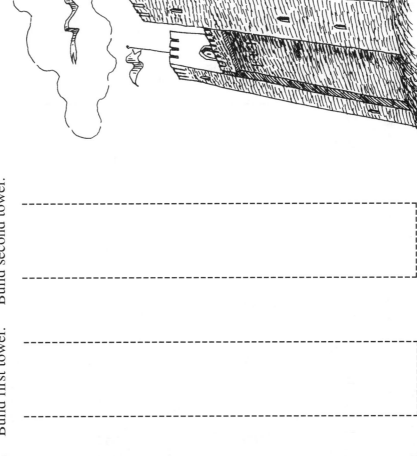

Build first tower.　　Build second tower.

Rebuild one or both towers if needed. Compare the fraction towers.

1. $\dfrac{3}{4} - \dfrac{2}{3} =$ _____

2. $\dfrac{5}{6} - \dfrac{1}{12} =$ _____

3. $\dfrac{3}{4} - \dfrac{5}{12} =$ _____

4. $\dfrac{9}{10} - \dfrac{3}{5} =$ _____

5. $\dfrac{5}{8} - \dfrac{1}{4} =$ _____

6. $\dfrac{5}{6} - \dfrac{7}{12} =$ _____

ESTIMATING DIFFERENCES

Name _____

Build and draw fraction towers for both fractions. Estimate to see how much taller one fraction tower is than the other. Circle **0**, **$\frac{1}{2}$**, or **1**. Then find the exact differences if you can.

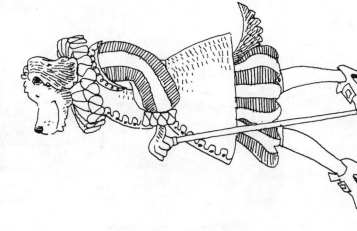

© Learning Resources, Inc.

1. $\dfrac{7}{12} - \dfrac{1}{6}$ is about   0   (**$\frac{1}{2}$**)   1

1

Difference

$\frac{1}{12}$
$\frac{1}{12}$
$\frac{1}{12}$
$\frac{1}{12}$
$\frac{1}{12}$
$\frac{1}{12}$
$\frac{1}{12}$

$\frac{1}{6}$

Build $\frac{7}{12}$.   Build $\frac{1}{6}$.

Estimate the difference.
Rebuild $\frac{1}{6}$ as $\frac{2}{12}$.

The exact difference is _____.

2. $\dfrac{4}{5} - \dfrac{3}{4}$ is about   0 $\frac{1}{2}$ 1

Difference {

$\frac{1}{5}$
$\frac{1}{5}$
$\frac{1}{5}$
$\frac{1}{5}$

$\frac{1}{4}$
$\frac{1}{4}$
$\frac{1}{4}$

Build $\frac{4}{5}$.   Build $\frac{3}{4}$.

Estimate the difference.
Since you cannot rebuild $\frac{4}{5}$ and $\frac{3}{4}$ using a common color, find equivalent fractions with a common denominator.

The exact difference is _____.

Think of a denominator whose factors are 5 and 4.

$\dfrac{4}{5} = \dfrac{\square}{\square}$ $\dfrac{3}{4} = \dfrac{\square}{\square}$

ESTIMATING MORE DIFFERENCES

Name _____

Use the grids to build and draw fraction towers for each fraction in the problems. Use the 1 fraction tower cube as a reference. Circle an estimate. Then find the exact difference if you can.

Problem		Circle estimate. Compare towers.	Find exact difference. Show your work.
1. $\dfrac{7}{8} - \dfrac{3}{4}$	→	$0 \quad \frac{1}{4} \quad \frac{1}{2} \quad \frac{3}{4} \quad 1$	_____
2. $\dfrac{2}{3} - \dfrac{1}{6}$	→	$0 \quad \frac{1}{4} \quad \frac{1}{2} \quad \frac{3}{4} \quad 1$	_____
3. $\dfrac{3}{5} - \dfrac{1}{6}$	→	$0 \quad \frac{1}{4} \quad \frac{1}{2} \quad \frac{3}{4} \quad 1$	_____
4. $\dfrac{7}{8} - \dfrac{1}{10}$	→	$0 \quad \frac{1}{4} \quad \frac{1}{2} \quad \frac{3}{4} \quad 1$	_____
5. $\dfrac{2}{5} - \dfrac{1}{3}$	→	$0 \quad \frac{1}{4} \quad \frac{1}{2} \quad \frac{3}{4} \quad 1$	_____

1

SUBTRACTING FROM MIXED NUMBERS

Name _____

Build fraction towers for the mixed number. Rebuild it if you cannot "take away" the fraction in each problem. Find the difference and simplify.

1. $1\frac{7}{12} - \frac{1}{2} = 1\frac{7}{12} - \frac{\square}{12} = 1\square\frac{\square}{12}$

Build $1\frac{7}{12}$.

$\frac{1}{12}$	$\frac{1}{12}$	$\frac{1}{12}$	$\frac{1}{12}$	$\frac{1}{12}$	$\frac{1}{12}$	$\frac{1}{12}$

Take away

Think: $\frac{1}{2} = \frac{6}{12}$

Take away $\frac{6}{12}$

1

1 red, 7 black – 6 black = ____ red, ____ black

2. $1\frac{4}{5} - 1\frac{3}{10} = 1\square\frac{\square}{10} - 1\frac{3}{10} = \square\frac{\square}{10}$

Build $1\frac{4}{5}$.

$\frac{1}{5}$	$\frac{1}{5}$	$\frac{1}{5}$	$\frac{1}{5}$

Take away

Take away $1\frac{3}{10}$

1

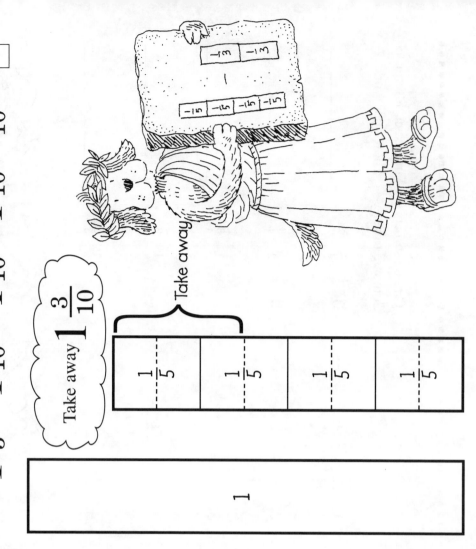

Rebuild.

1 red, ____ purple – 1 red, 3 purple = ____ purple = ____ pink

MORE SUBTRACTING FROM MIXED NUMBERS

Name _____

Use the grids to build the mixed numbers and then subtract. You may have to rebuild the mixed numbers before subtracting. Simplify the answers. Show your work on the blanks.

● ●

1

1 red and ☐ _____ _____
                        color

Build the first mixed number. Then "take away."

1. $1\frac{11}{12} - \frac{1}{3}$ = _____

2. $1\frac{1}{2} - \frac{2}{5}$ = _____

3. $1\frac{7}{8} - 1\frac{1}{4}$ = _____

4. $1\frac{3}{4} - \frac{2}{3}$ = _____

5. $1\frac{4}{5} - 1\frac{7}{10}$ = _____

6. $1\frac{1}{2} - \frac{5}{12}$ = _____

REGROUPING AND SUBTRACTING FRACTIONS WITH LIKE DENOMINATORS

Name _____

Build and draw the mixed number. Then rebuild and draw the mixed number without using a red cube. Take away the fraction amount, and record the difference. Write the difference in simplest form.

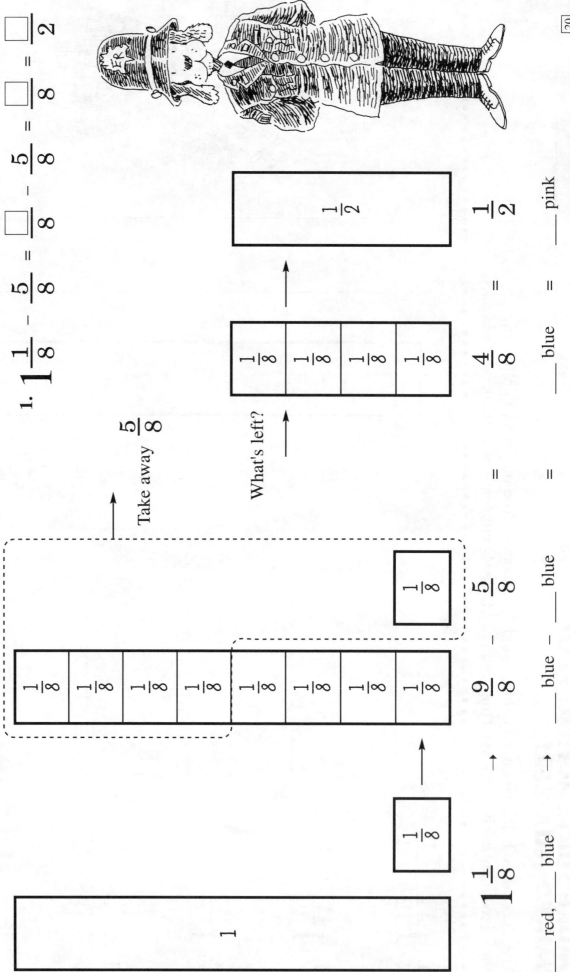

1. $1\dfrac{1}{8} - \dfrac{5}{8} = \dfrac{\square}{8} - \dfrac{5}{8} = \dfrac{\square}{8}$

$1\dfrac{1}{8}$

____ red, ____ blue   →   ____ blue   →   ____ blue   -   ____ blue

$\dfrac{9}{8}$ - $\dfrac{5}{8}$

Take away $\dfrac{5}{8}$

What's left?

$\dfrac{4}{8}$ =   ____ blue   = $\dfrac{1}{2}$ =   ____ pink

REGROUPING AND SUBTRACTING MORE FRACTIONS WITH LIKE DENOMINATORS

Use the grids below to find the differences. Write the differences in simplest form.

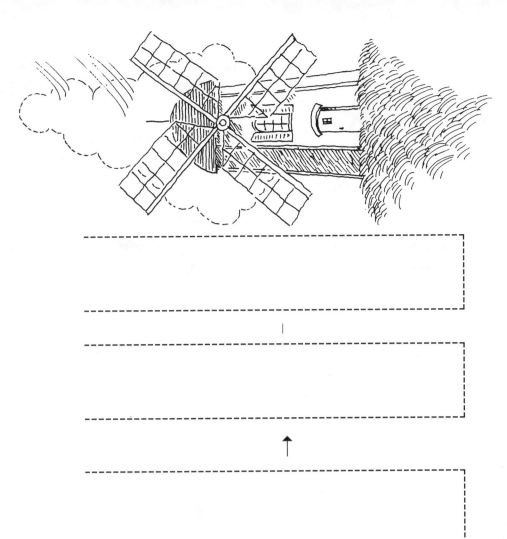

mixed number → regrouped – fraction = difference
mixed number

1. $1\frac{1}{4} - \frac{3}{4} =$ _____

2. $1\frac{2}{5} - \frac{3}{5} =$ _____

3. $1\frac{7}{12} - \frac{10}{12} =$ _____

4. $1\frac{1}{10} - \frac{7}{10} =$ _____

5. $1\frac{1}{6} - \frac{5}{6} =$ _____

6. $1\frac{5}{12} - \frac{11}{12} =$ _____

Try this one.

7. $2\frac{3}{10} - 1\frac{7}{10} =$ _____

REGROUPING AND SUBTRACTING FRACTIONS WITH UNLIKE DENOMINATORS

Name _____

Build and draw the mixed number. Then rebuild and draw the mixed number without using a red cube. Take away the fraction amount, and record the difference. Write the difference in simplest form.

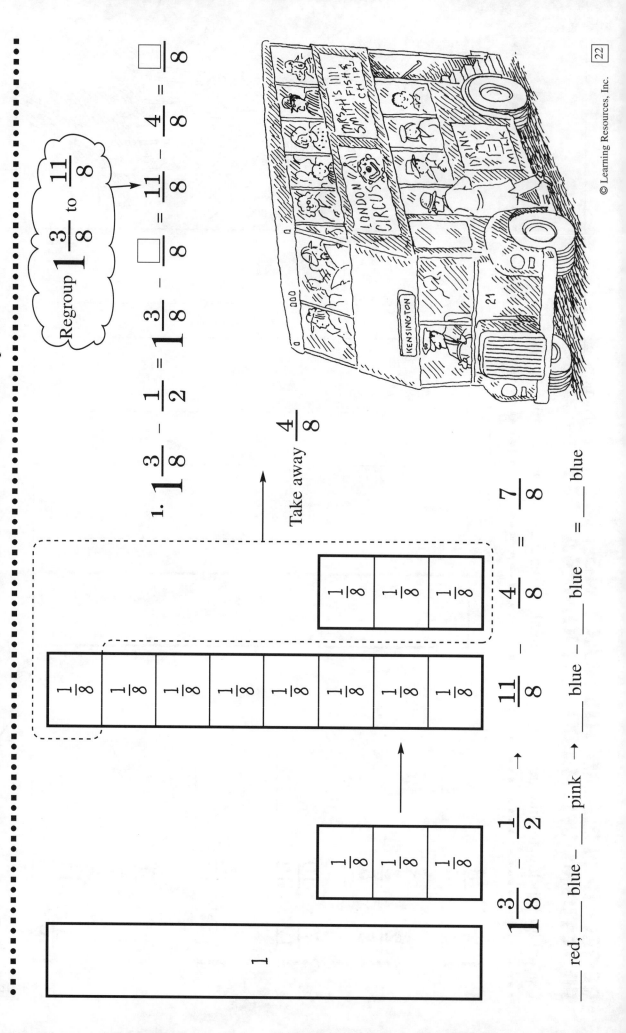

Regroup $1\dfrac{3}{8}$ to $\dfrac{11}{8}$

1. $1\dfrac{3}{8} - \dfrac{1}{2} = 1\dfrac{3}{8}$

$\dfrac{\square}{8} = 1\dfrac{3}{8}$

$\dfrac{11}{8} - \dfrac{4}{8} = \dfrac{\square}{8}$

Take away $\dfrac{4}{8}$

$\dfrac{11}{8} \qquad \dfrac{4}{8} = \dfrac{7}{8}$

___ red, ___ blue – ___ pink → ___ blue – ___ blue = ___ blue

REGROUPING AND SUBTRACTING MORE FRACTIONS WITH UNLIKE DENOMINATORS

Use the grids below to find the differences. Write the differences in simplest form.

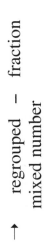

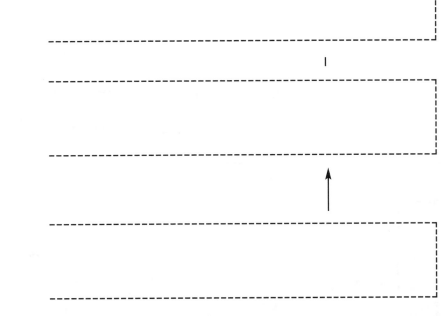

mixed number	$\rightarrow$ regrouped mixed number	$-$ fraction

$$\boxed{\qquad 1 \qquad}$$

1. $1\dfrac{5}{12} - \dfrac{1}{2} = $ _____

2. $1\dfrac{1}{3} - \dfrac{11}{12} = $ _____

3. $1\dfrac{1}{2} - \dfrac{7}{10} = $ _____

4. $1\dfrac{7}{12} - \dfrac{3}{4} = $ _____

5. $1\dfrac{3}{10} - \dfrac{1}{2} = $ _____

6. $1\dfrac{1}{2} - \dfrac{5}{6} = $ _____

SUBTRACTING WITH MIXED NUMBERS

Name _____

Build and draw the mixed number. Then rebuild it without using a red cube.
Take away the fraction amount and record the difference in simplest form.

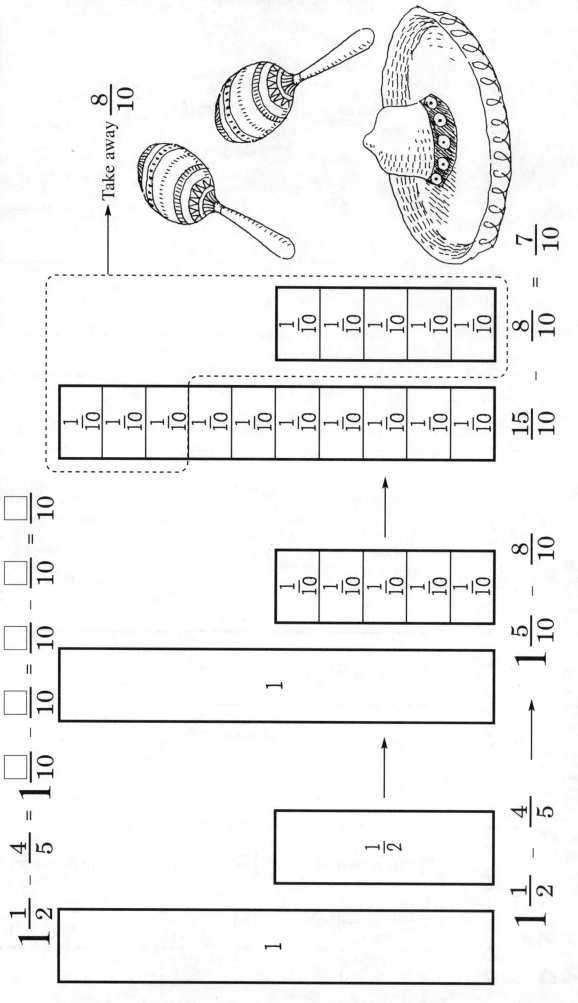

$$1 \frac{1}{2} - \frac{4}{5} = 1 \frac{\boxed{}}{10} - \frac{\boxed{}}{10} = \frac{\boxed{}}{10} - \frac{\boxed{}}{10} = \frac{\boxed{}}{10}$$

$$1 \frac{1}{2} - \frac{4}{5} \longrightarrow 1 \frac{5}{10} - \frac{8}{10}$$

$$\frac{15}{10} - \frac{8}{10} = \frac{7}{10}$$

Take away $\frac{8}{10}$

____ red, ____ pink – ____ green → ____ red, ____ purple – ____ purple – 8 purple = 7 purple

MORE SUBTRACTING WITH MIXED NUMBERS

Name _____

Use the grids below to find the differences. Write the differences in simplest form.

1. $1\frac{1}{3} - \frac{3}{4} = $ _____

2. $1\frac{2}{5} - \frac{1}{2} = $ _____

3. $1\frac{1}{12} - \frac{1}{2} = $ _____

4. $1\frac{1}{4} - \frac{1}{3} = $ _____

5. $2\frac{2}{3} - \frac{1}{2} = $ _____

6. $1\frac{1}{2} - \frac{3}{5} = $ _____

1

mixed number $\longrightarrow$ regrouped mixed number $-$ fraction

KEEP ON SUBTRACTING WITH MIXED NUMBERS

Name _____

Find the differences. Show your work on the blanks. Write the differences in simplest form.

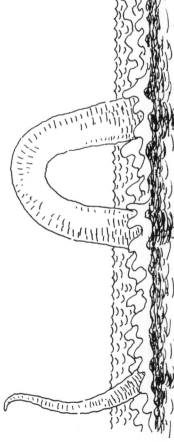

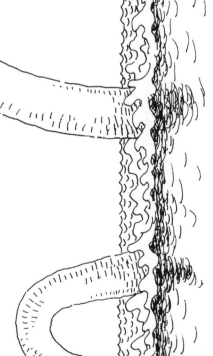

1. $1\dfrac{3}{8} - \dfrac{3}{4} =$ _____

2. $1\dfrac{1}{2} - \dfrac{2}{3} =$ _____

3. $1\dfrac{1}{12} - \dfrac{1}{6} =$ _____

4. $1\dfrac{1}{4} - \dfrac{7}{8} =$ _____

EVEN MORE SUBTRACTING WITH MIXED NUMBERS

Name _____

Find the differences. Show your work on the blanks. Write the differences in simplest form.

1. $1\dfrac{1}{10} - \dfrac{2}{5} =$ _____

2. $1\dfrac{1}{12} - \dfrac{1}{2} =$ _____

3. $1\dfrac{1}{8} - \dfrac{3}{4} =$ _____

4. $1\dfrac{2}{3} - \dfrac{11}{12} =$ _____

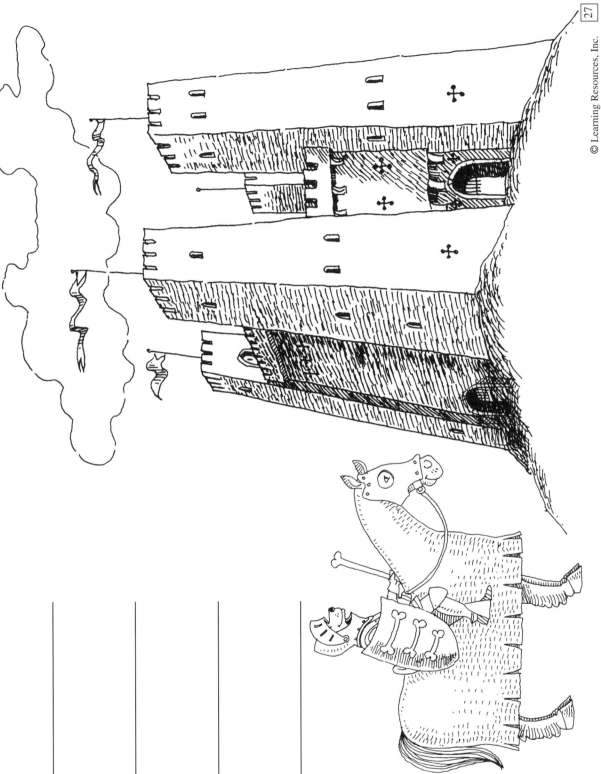

FRACTION SUBTRACTION ACTION

Name _____

Use the Fraction Tower Cubes to find the differences in simplest form for each problem.
Cross out the differences on the Fraction Subtraction Grid. Choose problems at random.
When you get 4 differences in a row, column, or diagonal, you're done!

• ▪ •

1. $\dfrac{7}{10} - \dfrac{2}{5} =$ _____

2. $1\dfrac{1}{6} - \dfrac{1}{4} =$ _____

3. $1\dfrac{2}{3} - \dfrac{11}{12} =$ _____

4. $\dfrac{7}{12} - \dfrac{1}{2} =$ _____

5. $\dfrac{4}{5} - \dfrac{1}{10} =$ _____

6. $1\dfrac{1}{8} - \dfrac{1}{2} =$ _____

7. $1\dfrac{5}{8} - \dfrac{3}{4} =$ _____

8. $1\dfrac{1}{5} - \dfrac{1}{10} =$ _____

9. $1\dfrac{5}{12} - \dfrac{3}{4} =$ _____

10. $\dfrac{4}{6} - \dfrac{5}{12} =$ _____

11. $1\dfrac{1}{2} - \dfrac{2}{3} =$ _____

12. $\dfrac{4}{5} - \dfrac{3}{10} =$ _____

Fraction Subtraction Grid

$\dfrac{11}{12}$	$\dfrac{7}{8}$	$\dfrac{1}{2}$	$\dfrac{3}{4}$
$\dfrac{1}{3}$	$\dfrac{7}{10}$	$\dfrac{1}{4}$	$\dfrac{5}{8}$
$\dfrac{5}{6}$	$\dfrac{1}{6}$	$\dfrac{2}{3}$	$\dfrac{1}{8}$
$\dfrac{3}{10}$	$1\dfrac{1}{10}$	$\dfrac{1}{10}$	$\dfrac{1}{12}$

ADDITION AND SUBTRACTION ACTION

Name _____

Use the Fraction Tower Cubes to find the sums and differences in simplest form for each problem. Cross out the answers on the Addition and Subtraction Grid. Choose problems at random. When you get 4 answers in a row, column, or diagonal, you're done!

1. $\dfrac{7}{12} + \dfrac{3}{4} =$ _____

2. $1\dfrac{1}{2} - \dfrac{5}{6} =$ _____

3. $\dfrac{1}{3} + \dfrac{1}{2} =$ _____

4. $\dfrac{11}{12} - \dfrac{5}{6} =$ _____

5. $\dfrac{3}{10} + \dfrac{1}{2} =$ _____

6. $\dfrac{5}{12} - \dfrac{1}{4} =$ _____

7. $1\dfrac{7}{12} - \dfrac{2}{3} =$ _____

8. $\dfrac{3}{4} + \dfrac{5}{8} =$ _____

9. $1\dfrac{1}{6} - \dfrac{3}{4} =$ _____

10. $1\dfrac{1}{4} - \dfrac{3}{8} =$ _____

11. $1\dfrac{1}{6} + \dfrac{1}{2} =$ _____

12. $\dfrac{4}{5} - \dfrac{7}{10} =$ _____

Addition and Subtraction Grid

$\dfrac{5}{6}$	$\dfrac{1}{8}$	$\dfrac{7}{8}$	$\dfrac{1}{12}$
$\dfrac{1}{5}$	$\dfrac{1}{6}$	$1\dfrac{2}{3}$	$\dfrac{1}{10}$
$\dfrac{2}{3}$	$\dfrac{7}{12}$	$\dfrac{5}{12}$	$\dfrac{11}{12}$
$1\dfrac{3}{8}$	$\dfrac{4}{5}$	$\dfrac{3}{8}$	$1\dfrac{1}{3}$

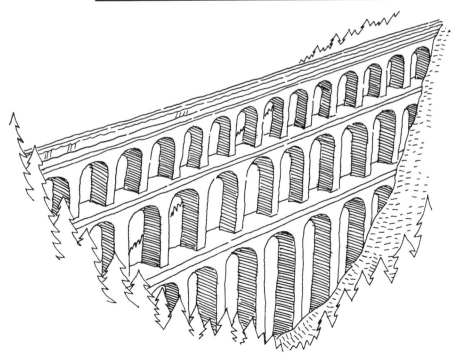

SPIN-A-DIFFERENCE GAME

Name _____

What will we need?
- 2 sets of Fraction Tower Cubes
- paper clip and pencil, or clear spinner
- 10 markers, 5 for each player

Who will play?
- 2 players

How will we play?
- Each player chooses a Player Board below and places 5 markers next to it.
- At each turn, each player spins the spinner and subtracts the fraction indicated from $1\frac{1}{2}$.
- Players must use the Fraction Tower Cubes to find the differences.
- Each player marks the difference for each round on his or her Player Board with a marker. If a difference is already marked with a marker, the player loses the turn. If the player marks a difference incorrectly, the other player can challenge the answer. If an answer is challenged and is incorrect, no marker is placed.

Who will win?
- The first player to show 5 differences on their Player Board.

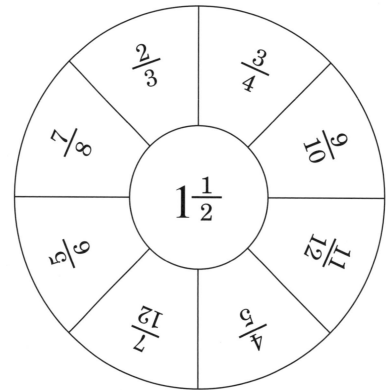

Player Board 1
$\frac{7}{12}$
$\frac{3}{5}$
$\frac{5}{8}$
$\frac{2}{3}$
$\frac{7}{10}$
$\frac{3}{4}$
$\frac{5}{6}$
$\frac{11}{12}$

Player Board 2
$\frac{7}{12}$
$\frac{3}{5}$
$\frac{5}{8}$
$\frac{2}{3}$
$\frac{7}{10}$
$\frac{3}{4}$
$\frac{5}{6}$
$\frac{11}{12}$

Spinner values: $\frac{2}{3}$, $\frac{3}{4}$, $\frac{9}{10}$, $\frac{11}{12}$, $\frac{4}{5}$, $\frac{7}{12}$, $\frac{5}{9}$, $\frac{7}{8}$ around center $1\frac{1}{2}$

TAKE AWAY TOWERS GAME

Name _____

What will we need?
- 2 sets of Fraction Tower Cubes
- bag or sack
- paper and pencil

Who will play?
- 2 players

How will we play?
- Pick a level of difficulty for the game. Then place the following colors of Fraction Tower Cubes in the bag. Unsnap the towers into individual fraction cubes.

Easy Game	Average Game	Hard Game	
pink	pink	pink	teal
green	yellow	orange	black
purple	blue	yellow	

- Without looking, each player takes a turn pulling a single cube from the bag until each player has pulled out 6 cubes.

- Each player thinks of a subtraction problem that uses his/her cubes to make the smallest difference. That is, each player builds 2 fraction towers with his/her cubes and compares the heights. Then the players write a subtraction number sentence for their towers.

- The player having the smallest difference receives 1 point. If both players have the same difference, they both receive a point.

Who will win?
- After 10 rounds, the player with more points is the winner.

SELECTED SOLUTIONS

● ●

Page 8: 1. $\frac{4}{5} - \frac{1}{10} = \frac{8}{10} - \frac{1}{10} = \frac{7}{10}$

2. $\frac{2}{3} - \frac{1}{4} = \frac{8}{12} - \frac{3}{12} = \frac{5}{12}$

Page 9: 1. $\frac{9}{12} - \frac{1}{6} = \frac{9}{12} - \frac{2}{12} = \frac{7}{12}$ 2. $\frac{7}{8} - \frac{1}{2} = \frac{7}{8} - \frac{4}{8} = \frac{3}{8}$

3. $\frac{2}{3} - \frac{1}{12} = \frac{8}{12} - \frac{1}{12} = \frac{7}{12}$ 4. $\frac{1}{2} - \frac{1}{8} = \frac{4}{8} - \frac{1}{8} = \frac{3}{8}$

5. $\frac{11}{12} - \frac{1}{2} = \frac{11}{12} - \frac{6}{12} = \frac{5}{12}$ 6. $\frac{1}{2} - \frac{1}{12} = \frac{6}{12} - \frac{1}{12} = \frac{5}{12}$

7. $\frac{2}{3} - \frac{1}{2} = \frac{4}{6} - \frac{3}{6} = \frac{1}{6}$ 8. $\frac{5}{6} - \frac{1}{4} = \frac{10}{12} - \frac{3}{12} = \frac{7}{12}$

Page 10: 1. $\frac{11}{12} - \frac{2}{3} = \frac{11}{12} - \frac{8}{12} = \frac{3}{12} = \frac{1}{4}$

2. $\frac{1}{2} - \frac{1}{10} = \frac{5}{10} - \frac{1}{10} = \frac{4}{10} = \frac{2}{5}$

Page 11: 1. $\frac{7}{10} - \frac{1}{5} = \frac{7}{10} - \frac{2}{10} = \frac{5}{10} = \frac{1}{2}$

2. $\frac{1}{2} - \frac{1}{3} = \frac{3}{6} - \frac{2}{6} = \frac{1}{6} = \frac{1}{6}$

3. $\frac{9}{10} - \frac{1}{2} = \frac{9}{10} - \frac{5}{10} = \frac{4}{10} = \frac{2}{5}$

4. $\frac{7}{12} - \frac{1}{4} = \frac{7}{12} - \frac{3}{12} = \frac{4}{12} = \frac{1}{3}$

5. $\frac{3}{4} - \frac{1}{6} = \frac{9}{12} - \frac{2}{12} = \frac{7}{12}$

6. $\frac{5}{6} - \frac{3}{4} = \frac{10}{12} - \frac{9}{12} = \frac{1}{12}$

Page 12: 1. $\frac{7}{8} - \frac{1}{2} = \frac{7}{8} - \frac{4}{8} = \frac{3}{8}$

2. $\frac{2}{3} - \frac{5}{12} = \frac{8}{12} - \frac{5}{12} = \frac{3}{12} = \frac{1}{4}$

Page 13: 1. $\frac{3}{4} - \frac{1}{8} = \frac{6}{8} - \frac{1}{8} = \frac{5}{8}$ 2. $\frac{2}{3} - \frac{1}{4} = \frac{8}{12} - \frac{3}{12} = \frac{5}{12}$

Page 14: 1. $\frac{11}{12} - \frac{2}{3} = \frac{11}{12} - \frac{8}{12} = \frac{3}{12} = \frac{1}{4}$

2. $\frac{4}{5} - \frac{3}{10} = \frac{8}{10} - \frac{3}{10} = \frac{5}{10} = \frac{1}{2}$

Page 15: 1. $\frac{1}{12}$ 2. $\frac{3}{4}$ 3. $\frac{1}{3}$ 4. $\frac{3}{10}$ 5. $\frac{3}{8}$ 6. $\frac{1}{4}$

Page 16: 1. est: $\frac{1}{2}$; diff: $\frac{7}{12} - \frac{2}{12} = \frac{5}{12}$

2. est: 0; equivalent fractions $\frac{4}{5} = \frac{16}{20}$ and $\frac{3}{4} = \frac{15}{20}$; diff: $\frac{16}{20} - \frac{15}{20} = \frac{1}{20}$

Page 17: 1. est: 0; diff: $\frac{7}{8} - \frac{6}{8} = \frac{1}{8}$

2. est: $\frac{1}{2}$; diff: $\frac{4}{6} - \frac{1}{6} = \frac{3}{6} = \frac{1}{2}$

3. est: $\frac{1}{2}$; diff: $\frac{18}{30} - \frac{5}{30} = \frac{13}{30}$

4. est: $\frac{3}{4}$; diff: $\frac{35}{40} - \frac{4}{40} = \frac{31}{40}$

5. est: 0; diff: $\frac{6}{15} - \frac{5}{15} = \frac{1}{15}$

Page 18: 1. $1\frac{7}{12} - \frac{6}{12} = 1\frac{1}{12}$; 1 red, 1 black

2. $1\frac{8}{10} - 1\frac{3}{10} = \frac{5}{10} = \frac{1}{2}$; 1 red, 8 purple - 1 red, 3 purple = 5 purple = 1 pink

Page 19: 1. $= 1\frac{11}{12} - \frac{4}{12} = 1\frac{7}{12}$ 2. $= 1\frac{5}{10} - \frac{4}{10} = 1\frac{1}{10}$

3. $= 1\frac{7}{8} - 1\frac{2}{8} = \frac{5}{8}$ 4. $= 1\frac{9}{12} - \frac{8}{12} = 1\frac{1}{12}$

5. $= 1\frac{8}{10} - 1\frac{7}{10} = \frac{1}{10}$ 6. $= 1\frac{6}{12} - \frac{5}{12} = 1\frac{1}{12}$

Page 20: $1\frac{1}{8} - \frac{5}{8} = \frac{9}{8} - \frac{5}{8} = \frac{4}{8} = \frac{1}{2}$

1 red, 1 blue (9 blue - 5 blue = 4 blue = 1 pink)

Page 21: 1. $\frac{5}{4} - \frac{3}{4} = \frac{2}{4} = \frac{1}{2}$

2. $= \frac{7}{5} - \frac{3}{5} = \frac{4}{5}$

3. $= \frac{19}{12} - \frac{10}{12} = \frac{9}{12} = \frac{3}{4}$

4. $= \frac{11}{10} - \frac{7}{10} = \frac{4}{10} = \frac{2}{5}$

5. $= \frac{7}{6} - \frac{5}{6} = \frac{2}{6} = \frac{1}{3}$

6. $= \frac{17}{12} - \frac{11}{12} = \frac{6}{12} = \frac{1}{2}$

7. $= \frac{23}{10} - \frac{17}{10} = \frac{6}{10} = \frac{3}{5}$

Page 22: 1. $1\frac{3}{8} - \frac{1}{2} = 1\frac{3}{8} - \frac{4}{8} = \frac{11}{8} - \frac{4}{8} = \frac{7}{8}$

1 red, 3 blue - 1 pink → 11 blue - 4 blue = 7 blue

Page 23: 1. $= 1\frac{5}{12} - \frac{6}{12} = \frac{17}{12} - \frac{6}{12} = \frac{11}{12}$

2. $= 1\frac{4}{12} - \frac{11}{12} = \frac{16}{12} - \frac{11}{12} = \frac{5}{12}$

3. $= 1\frac{5}{10} - \frac{7}{10} = \frac{15}{10} - \frac{7}{10} = \frac{8}{10} = \frac{4}{5}$

4. $= 1\frac{7}{12} - \frac{9}{12} = \frac{19}{12} - \frac{9}{12} = \frac{10}{12} = \frac{5}{6}$

5. $= 1\frac{3}{10} - \frac{5}{10} = \frac{13}{10} - \frac{5}{10} = \frac{8}{10} = \frac{4}{5}$

6. $= 1\frac{3}{6} - \frac{5}{6} = \frac{9}{6} - \frac{5}{6} = \frac{4}{6} = \frac{2}{3}$

Page 24: $1\frac{1}{2} - \frac{4}{5} = 1\frac{5}{10} - \frac{8}{10} = \frac{15}{10} - \frac{8}{10} = \frac{7}{10}$ 1 red, 1 pink – 4 green → 1 red, 5 purple - 8 purple = 15 purple – 8 purple = 7 purple

Page 25: 1. $= 1\frac{4}{12} - \frac{9}{12} = \frac{16}{12} - \frac{9}{12} = \frac{7}{12}$

2. $= 1\frac{4}{10} - \frac{9}{10} = \frac{14}{10} - \frac{5}{10} = \frac{9}{10}$

3. $= 1\frac{1}{12} - \frac{6}{12} = \frac{13}{12} - \frac{6}{12} = \frac{7}{12}$

4. $= 1\frac{3}{12} - \frac{4}{12} = \frac{15}{12} - \frac{4}{12} = \frac{11}{12}$

5. $= 2\frac{4}{6} - 1\frac{3}{6} = 1\frac{1}{6}$

6. $= 1\frac{5}{10} - \frac{6}{10} = \frac{15}{10} - \frac{6}{10} = \frac{9}{10}$

Page 26: 1. $= \frac{11}{8} - \frac{6}{8} = \frac{5}{8}$ 2. $= \frac{9}{6} - \frac{4}{6} = \frac{5}{6}$

3. $= \frac{13}{12} - \frac{2}{12} = \frac{11}{12}$ 4. $= \frac{10}{8} - \frac{7}{8} = \frac{3}{8}$

Page 27: 1. $= \frac{11}{10} - \frac{4}{10} = \frac{7}{10}$ 2. $\frac{13}{12} - \frac{6}{12} = \frac{7}{12}$

3. $= \frac{9}{8} - \frac{6}{8} = \frac{3}{8}$ 4. $= \frac{20}{12} - \frac{11}{12} = \frac{9}{12} = \frac{3}{4}$

Page 28: *Fraction Subtraction Action*

1. $\frac{3}{10}$ 2. $\frac{11}{12}$ 3. $\frac{3}{4}$ 4. $\frac{1}{12}$ 5. $\frac{7}{10}$ 6. $\frac{5}{8}$

7. $\frac{7}{8}$ 8. $1\frac{1}{10}$ 9. $\frac{2}{3}$ 10. $\frac{1}{4}$ 11. $\frac{5}{6}$ 12. $\frac{1}{2}$

Page 29: *Addition and Subtraction Action*

1. $1\frac{1}{3}$ 2. $\frac{2}{3}$ 3. $\frac{5}{6}$ 4. $\frac{1}{12}$ 5. $\frac{4}{5}$ 6. $\frac{1}{6}$

7. $\frac{11}{12}$ 8. $1\frac{3}{8}$ 9. $\frac{5}{12}$ 10. $\frac{7}{8}$ 11. $1\frac{2}{3}$ 12. $\frac{1}{10}$

Page 30: *Spin-A-Difference Game*

$1\frac{1}{2} - \frac{11}{12} = \frac{7}{12}$ $1\frac{1}{2} - \frac{9}{10} = \frac{3}{5}$

$1\frac{1}{2} - \frac{7}{8} = \frac{5}{8}$ $1\frac{1}{2} - \frac{5}{6} = \frac{2}{3}$

$1\frac{1}{2} - \frac{4}{5} = \frac{7}{10}$ $1\frac{1}{2} - \frac{3}{4} = \frac{3}{4}$

$1\frac{1}{2} - \frac{2}{3} = \frac{5}{6}$ $1\frac{1}{2} - \frac{7}{12} = \frac{11}{12}$